CW00541289

Through The Storm

Through The Storm

by
Martine Ashley

To every broken soul who needs a little reassurance that it gets better.

<u>REMINDER.</u>

You're weak now, you'll be stronger later.

Allow yourself to feel all of the emotions in your head & your heart.

Feel all the pain, feel all the sadness, and feel all of that anger inside of you.

& once you've felt it and you're in that moment of your emotions going wild,

Let it go.

Acknowledge that they're there and then tell them to get the hell out.

You have no room for them in your heart anymore.

Dear reader,

I know you've probably gone through hell & back.

I know you've had times where you've questioned yourself.

You've had relationships & friendships that have drained you.

I know sometimes you've looked in the mirror & hated what you saw.

I know you've felt like you doing your absolute best just isn't good enough.

I know what it's like to hate the life you live for whatever reason.

I know what it's like to feel your heart breaking into pieces.

You feel like it will never get better.

You feel like this pain is going to hurt like this forever.

You feel like you were dealt the worst cards ever & no one could ever understand.

Well I understand, I've been there.

And I want you to know that it gets better.

I want you to stop doubting yourself, go off your instincts & go for everything you deserve.

I want you to be so happy it not only makes up for all the bad that you've suffered but it exceeds it, it overflows.

I want you to allow yourself to deserve better.

I want you to smile & laugh more because everyone including yourself deserves to see that beautiful side of you.

I know that you're tired.

I know giving up sounds like the way to go right now, it's easier & maybe just maybe you won't feel the pain anymore reminding you had bad it is right now if you just throw in the towel.
So even though it may take everything out of you, I want you to keep going.
Even if you feel there's no reason at all to keep going, I want you to fight it.
I want you to know that someone knows your pain, someone knows that emptiness that you feel right now and not only do they understand it and have lived it, but they made it out the other side.
Through all the rainy days and thunderstorm nights, someone woke up to the sun shining brighter than ever and I'll admit, it still wasn't perfect.
It didn't erase everything that they'd been through but for a little while, everything was okay, the pain hurt a little less & they made it.
So please don't give up.

<u>I miss me.</u>
I miss how happy I used to always be.
That me that was so vibrant, so enthusiastic, and so ready to take on the world by any means necessary.
She was so strong.
That me that saw so much good in the world and in people.
That me that saw the world in the half full instead of half empty perspective.
She was so full of joy & life.
I miss that me that wanted to love with her whole heart and soul.
That me that couldn't wait to fall in love because of how beautiful she's imagined & pictured it for so long.
That me saw so much beauty, passion & fire in love.
I miss her.
That me that wasn't afraid of getting back out there knowing there was a possibility of her falling flat on her face again and again and again, but she did it anyways because she always felt love was worth every fall she'd ever take.
I miss how she wasn't afraid to open up & let someone enter her life & world because she knew that no matter what, good or bad, they would bring something new out of her & into her life that she would carry around for the rest of her life to make her a better version of herself.
She dreamt so big with everything she put her mind to.
God, I miss her with every inch of my body.
I guess I just miss the old me before the world, love, heartbreak, and pain got a hold of her.

4

<u>Just let me heal.</u>

'Stop telling me that I need to let go and move on already. Stop telling me how bad he was for me in the first place. It took every inch of my body to leave him. You don't get it. He was and still to this day is my everything. We had plans. For the last couple of years, he was all that I knew. He was my comfort zone. I knew what to expect waking up to him every morning, good or bad. Yeah there were bad times, some horrible times in there as well trust me I know, I was there. But there were some amazing times as well. Although the bad times outweighed the good, it doesn't erase the good that was there. So I'm so sorry if I'm not moving on as quickly as I should or as quickly as you'd want me to. I'm truly sorry, but I'm not. A huge part of my life, my heart, and my soul is gone in a blink of an eye and that was all me, my decision. So as I recover and try every day to stop trying to blame myself for my failed relationship, I need you to be patient with me. My heart and I are going to need some time to fix these broken pieces. I know you have my best intentions at heart, but I need you to just please let me heal.'

<u>I'm letting you go.</u>
I've been avoiding this for so long.
Hoping and praying that things would change between us.
Pleading with everything in me for us not to have to go down this route, but it's here.
It's not because I don't love you, because lord knows that I do.
It's not because I don't care, because I've fought with every ounce in me for us.
I pray you don't think that this is because of you.
I hope you don't ever place blame or responsibility for this on yourself.
We've both put in an amount of fight that was one for the ages.
I know you love me, and trust me I love you.
But as time has gone by I've realized that us loving each other, it isn't enough.
I know this is what has to be done.
Not just for me, not just for you, but for the both us of.
I'm letting you go because we both deserve so much more.
I want to us both to be happy.
We had such a good run.
I don't want it to be overshadowed by all of the bad.
I don't want to start hating you or regretting you or this tremendous love that we shared together.
Please don't hate me for something you don't understand or see yet.
It's time.
I can't believe it, I'm really letting you go.

6

"I'm sorry."

'I don't want you to apologize. I don't want your tears. I don't want your sad face trying to guilt me into forgetting everything that just happened. Sorry can't fix this one. I'm tired of hearing how sorry you are after every mistake that you make. For once I just want you to actually be sorry. I want to see it in your eyes that you're sorry. I want you to show me that you're sorry. I want you to realize what you have right in front of you, and stop putting me through this same shit over and over again. I'm tired of hearing how sorry you are because nothing changes afterwards or even if it changes, it changes for a second which leads me to believe that you're changing just for you to revert back to the same old same old. You want to tell me that you're sorry, you want to prove it to me. Show me. I don't want gifts, I don't want money; I want changed behavior. I want to see it. For once, show me that you're sorry. Show me that you care. Show me that you don't want to lose me because I just can't take your word for it anymore.'

I hate the way I remember you.

'I hate the way that I remember you. All I can think of is the bad when it comes to you. When you made me cry, when you made me hate myself, when you broke me and left me, but I know that's not all we consisted of. I know we had some amazing times. I know we had times where you made me laugh till I cried. I know we had moments where I looked into your eyes and felt this undeniable, indescribable, never wanting it to end type of love that we had for one another. When I look at you now, when I think about you now, all I see is the bad and I hate it. I hate that we let it get to this point where I hate thinking about you because all it does is bring me pain and unhappiness. It causes me relive some horrific moments & I hate that we let it get this far.'

I feel sorry for you.

I feel sorry for you because it takes almost destroying women to make you feel like more of a man.

I feel sorry for you because despite what you think, how you act, or how you want to be perceived as, you're not a man.

You're nowhere close to being a man.

You're a little boy trying to fill shoes you clearly can't.

I feel sorry for you because you're weak.

Instead of dealing with your past traumas and healing, you choose to destroy innocent people, innocent people who could've loved you so well.

I feel sorry for you because there's no hope for you.

You sit there & you're okay with who you are.

You point fingers in every direction but your own.

You feel as if you're the high and mighty,

When in reality you're really just a scared little boy who never found his way.

More than anything, although I feel so sorry for you.

I feel sorry for the next person that's going to have to suffer like I did when it came to you.

I want to move on already.

'I just want to move on. I want to be over this. I don't want to spend the rest of my life holding this over my head & never really living. I want to let this go. I want to heal, I want to forgive you, I want to forget this and move on with my life already. I don't want you to have this control over my life where I can't do anything without thinking of what you did or didn't do to or for me. You lost something so special so why do I feel like I'm the loser in this situation right now? Why does it seem like I'm the only one suffering? It's not fair. I want my life back before you ever came into the picture. I just want to be free. I want to breathe again.'

You missed out.

I want you to know that you missed out.

I have some issues I still need to work on.

I'm not proud of the things I stayed through & allowed.

I'm not the best version of myself just yet,

But see the difference between me & you,

I'm working every day to be that person.

While your content with your toxic ways.

I'm learning to forgive, to heal, to grow, and to let go.

It's going to be one hell of a journey, but the end results are going to be worth every tear I have to shed, every old memory I'm going to have to relive and heal from, and every person that I'm going to have to let go of.

So yea you may not have gotten the happiest, most secure, most peaceful version of me, but because of you, I got it.

I got that version of me.

I got her.

& sometime in the future someone else will get that version of me as well.

We'll both look back & laugh together on what you & I had,

And we'll both me more grateful because of it.

Because if it weren't for you,

Neither of us would've got this version of me.

So thank you I guess

From me and the person who realized what they had the first time.

I have some work to do on myself.

'I let so much of my past play such a huge role on my present, on me, on you. I've just been hurt so many times, it's so hard to just let that go. It's hard to try when all you think about in the back of your mind is if this person is going to hurt me as the rest have. What makes this so worse is that I can see you're a really good person, and I honestly feel like you could make me so happy if I wasn't so damaged. I don't want to hurt you, and I know you'd work overtime to try to make this work and that's what I love so much about you, but this isn't right for you. This isn't on you, this isn't your fault and you shouldn't have to pay the price for me not healing or my past pain. I've got some work to do on myself and I know you'll never understand, but there are some demons of mine that I have to fight on my own to get back to who I was or who I know I can be. I just want you to know, I could've loved so much and so hard if you were my first. I just know it.'

<u>REMINDER.</u>
Don't let the fact that you love this person
Blind you from what you know is being treated wrong or
right.
People can love you & treat you right at the same time.
There will be tough times in a relationship.
& you're going to have to be very forgiving at times.
But how you're treated by someone who claims to love
you,
Is very cut & clear.
Keep that in mind.

I need you to let me go.

'I'm exhausted, please just let me go. Let me move on, let me go be happy. It's not fair for me, for us to always be on your terms. Whenever you want to or whenever you're ready, I have to drop everything and be right there. And I know, I know I have to learn to be stronger, stand firmly on my own two feet and not allow it anymore, but I just need you to leave me alone. Let me be. You say you love me and from what I've seen from you & your actions, it has been the complete opposite of love. So I need you right now, I'm begging you right now to find whatever ounce of love that you claim to have for me in your heart, and let me go.'

Stop falling for potential.

When you love someone you have to love who they are
right now in front of you.

You have to be okay with them being that exact version of
themselves forever.

You can't love someone & hold them to your expectations
of how you pictured they'd be or want them to be.

That's not fair to you, and that's not fair to them.

People have the right to be who they want to be whether
you like it or not.

They have the right to change but they also have the right
to stay the exact same.

You have to decide if you're going to be okay with the
person standing right in front of you being that person
forever.

You can't hold people to the potential that YOU see in
them.

I know you just want the best for them and you want them
to be the best they can be.

But you can't make people be who you want them to be.

I trusted you.

'I trusted you. I told you things I never told anyone. I opened up to you more than I've ever opened up to anyone else. **You made me comfortable with trusting you just to break me down.** I trusted that not only would you go out of your way to protect me from anything or anyone who could hurt me, but that you would never put me in a position where I'd ever look at you as another human being who took advantage of my heart and broke me. You failed, miserably. You're the absolute worst kind of human being because you saw how uncomfortable I was speaking about it, you saw how difficult it was for me to open up, you saw how that pain affected my everyday life and not only did you sit there, listen, but you consoled me. You held my hand and you persuaded me that this was nothing like my past. You made me believe you were different just to use all of my pain against me & hurt me worse than I ever have been hurt before. So thank you, thanks for proving me right about you.'

Why it's okay to let go.

Letting go seems scary huh? You're letting go of this person that you've grown to love and you've gotten comfortable with them. I know. It's going to hurt like hell at first. You're going to feel like there's nothing anyone can say or do to make this process easier and you'll probably be right for a little while about it. Just to give you some peace for you stop worrying so much and just deal with this heartbreak; your heart doesn't stay broken forever, you will find happiness again, and this love that you've had with this person is nothing compared to the love you're going to receive from the right person when it's time.
I promise.
So let go & heal in peace.

<u>REMINDER.</u>

Choose to see the good in people even when all they've showcased is bad.

That's your heart, that's who you are & there's nothing wrong with that quality.

While choosing to see the good, there has to be a limitation.

Choose what to allow & choose what's deserving to be in your presence and in your life.

Just because you see some good doesn't equate to an entry pass into your life.

Don't be afraid to stand up for you.

Do not ever be afraid to stand up for yourself.
Stand up for yourself when you're unhappy.
Express when you're not satisfied.
Address when situations are being detrimental to any aspect of your life.
If you can't stand up for yourself,
If you can't stand up for your worth,
How can you ever expect anyone to take you seriously?
How can you ever expect anyone to take your worth serious & treat you accordingly?
Take a stand.
It's time to do right by you & your worth.

I'm choosing me.

This time, I'm choosing me.

I've chosen people over me for so long.

I've put people's needs & wants over mine for so long.

I've run dry trying to keep everyone else watered.

Even if I wanted to give, I have nothing left in me to give.

So I'm choosing me.

I'm choosing my happiness.

I'm choosing to finally chase & do things that make me smile & bring me excitement.

I'm choosing my needs.

I'm choosing to do what's best for me even if it bothers or interrupts my surroundings.

I'm choosing my wants.

I'm choosing to make my fragile heart as happy and as full of life as possible because it's what my heart & I deserve.

I'm choosing me because no one else ever did & I guess because of that, I never felt worthy enough to be chosen, until now.

I tried to hide from my demons.

I don't think I was ready for this, for us at all.
I rushed into this trying to escape and avoid dealing with
some scary things;
Some skeletons in my closet, some parts of my past I like
to try to forget.
But no matter how hard I try to be in the moment with you
& live in the present,
The past keeps calling, it's banging on the front door & it's
not going away.
I've hidden in every place I could possibly think of and it
finds me every single time just when I think I've finally
outsmarted it.
It's gotten to the point where I feel I have to stop running &
hiding & avoiding.
I think it's all come down to me having to face my demons
head first.
It terrifies me,
Having to go back and deal with the past that I've worked
so hard trying to bury.
But I'm more terrified that if I don't deal with it now, it's
going to haunt me for the rest of my life.
I don't want to live like this forever.
I don't want to have to hurt the people I love because I'm
too afraid to fight back.
What happened, happened and I have to deal with that.
I can't keep dragging down the people I love because of it.

I want you to know that I never meant to hurt you, I just wanted to stop hurting.

I have some pretty tough past battles I have to face, and I have to do it alone for me.

I'm not letting the past win anymore.

I'm done letting it control me and drag me back every time I feel I take a couple steps forward.

This is going to be the hardest, toughest, most painful battles I'll ever face, but I know that once I do; I'll finally be able to live the life I want to, the life I deserve.

Forgive yourself.

It's time to forgive yourself.
Sometimes we hold ourselves accountable a little too much.
We blame ourselves and we never learn to stop beating
ourselves up for it.
We indulge in the beating and never let it go.
As important as it is to forgive the people who hurt you,
It's just as important to forgive yourself for the pain you've
caused you or allowed from other people.
So you've made some huge mistakes when you were
young,
You can't hold that against yourself forever.
You didn't know better, and there was no way you
could've done better.
It's time to forgive yourself.
So you've made this mistake a couple of times, and
somehow deep down no matter how hard you try this one
little mistake keeps repeating itself and not only hurting
yourself but the people that you love surrounding you.
There is no road map for life. We live it, we learn from it
and we keep going.
Forgive yourself for giving it the absolute best that you
could and falling a little short this time around.
So you've allowed a ton of things you know now looking
back you didn't deserve.
Forgive yourself for not realizing your worth early on, for
allowing anything detrimental to you around you and for
sometimes just being plain old stupid.

We're all going to go through life. Sometimes we'll disappoint the people we love & sometimes we'll disappoint ourselves, but you know what the beauty of life is? We get to wake up on a brand new day & do things a little differently, a little better. You get the chance to fix things & be wiser. Forgive yourself today & let's put the energy into doing better tomorrow.

People get tired.
People get burned out.
So while you continue to do what you're doing.
Just know that people don't stick around forever
Especially if you don't give them something good to stick
around or hope for.

"Don't be like that. I know you miss me, us, and all the
good times we shared."

'You know what you're right, I do miss those nights alone
that I cried myself to sleep feeling worthless and lifeless
because of you. Oh no, how about those nights I use to beg
and plead with God and you to stop the pain because I felt
like I was dying on the inside. No wait, I really do miss those
fights we use to have where you'd degrade me, belittle me
and make me feel so stupid for wanting more or speaking up
for myself, yea those were great times. Better yet I miss
watching you make a fool out of me in front of everyone,
being laughed at, and embarrassed because you couldn't be
honest with me about anything. Wait, wait, wait, I kind of
miss looking in the mirror and questioning myself you
know? Asking myself why I wasn't good enough or what
wasn't I doing enough of to make us work. But you know
what I think I miss the most? Being angry, sad or miserable
all of the time, and if it wasn't sad or angry I was numb. You
know what, thanks though for bringing me back down
memory lane, those were amazing times huh? Amazing
times you probably don't even remember because if it didn't
benefit you in any kind of way you were gone in seconds
whether it was mentally, emotionally or physically, you were
gone. So no! I promise you I don't ever think about us, I
don't miss us and I damn sure don't miss you or the hell you
bought into my life.'

I am not your mother.
I am not your father.
I am not your past.
I will not be punished for their actions.
I am willing to love you, through the good & the bad,
But I am not & will not be your punching bag.

Dear guy that broke me,

I was in such a dark place when things ended between me &
you. It was such a lonely, cold, sad place. I had sunken so
deep into this dark place that I couldn't see the light
anymore. I dug myself into such a deep hole, I gave up ever
getting out. That's how impossible it was, how impossible it
felt when you left. I just wanted to let you know that through
hope, time & patience I slowly dug myself out of this hole. I
never thought I'd get to a place where I'm at peace. I'm at
peace with myself. I'm at peace with you and what happened
between us. I'm at peace with it all. I'll never know why you
did what you did, and I never thought I'd get to a place where
I don't care about the reasoning why, but here I am. I doubt
that you even care, but this is definitely more for me. You
didn't break me, I thought you did, but you didn't. You made
me stumble, you pushed me down, and you held me down
quite a few times, but I got back up and I kept moving. You
didn't break me, you made me stronger. You made me have
to look within myself and fight. You may have cracked me,
but I'm still here. So I'm not even going to thank you for it
because it was all me. You pushed me down, but I had to
find the will from within to get back up and move forward. I
hope you weren't expecting a letter that would make your
ego feel as big as it already is. This is more of "now you're
going to have to watch me shine like a star" letter. I guess
this is more of toot my own horn letter. I made it out.

REMINDER.

Love has no specific time limit.

Just because you've loved this person for 10 years doesn't mean this is who you were supposed to spend the rest of your life with.

This goes for Relationships, Family, and Friendships.

Stop forcing yourself to stick in unhappy, toxic, unsatisfied relationships out of loyalty or history or the amount of time that has been put in.

Don't rob yourself of the happiness you could have.

Life is too short.

Should've left me where I was.

'I wish you would've just left me where I was. You walked in and ruined everything. I was so good before you, it was great, and I was amazing. I had huge plans for myself and for my life. I was happy and you just had to walk in with your pretty smile & your charm and sweep me off my feet just to eventually throw me down and spit on me. I didn't ask for this, for you. You didn't have to come into my life that was your choice. You didn't have to stay in my life that was your choice. How do you walk into someone's life, destroy everything & walk away like nothing happened, as if nothing mattered?'

Through The Storm

You hate that you cannot control me anymore.

'You hate me now. I can see it in your face. You hate the fact that I don't need you anymore. You hate that I could really conquer the world without you. You can't handle the fact that I could not only do life without you, but I could kill it. I could be happy without you. I could chase my dreams and be successful. I can do whatever I want. I never needed you & I know deep down, it crushes your ego

31

<u>Time means nothing when your heart is being mistreated.</u>

There are no special relationship exceptions on why you should let people get away with mistreating you.

So you've loved them since you guys were kids;

If they've spent that many years "loving" you & they still don't know how to love you or treat you correctly? That says a lot more about their character and the way they feel about you deep down inside. Just because you're used to them doesn't mean it's okay to accept whatever.

So they're your first love, first kiss, first sexual experience, etc.

In life, there's so much growth that we encounter, so many lessons we have to learn, so many mistakes you have to make in order to be the person you envisioned yourself being. Yes, you loved them first but doesn't mean they'll be who you love last. Just because they were your first doesn't mean you're required to have to make it work when you're not in a good situation. Sometimes our firsts set us up, they prepare us for how we'll continue far after them and for ours lasts.

So you have kids together with this person;

Everything you do or say will have an impact on your kid's lives and majority of us know this from experience because we're still healing from what our parents put us through. Your kids, they'll look to you for how relationships are supposed to be. They'll have to heal from the traumas they witness. Be an example to them. If you wouldn't want your son or daughter to stick around & make it work, you shouldn't want it for yourself. Kids want to see their parents happy not miserable. It's okay to let go.

So you're married;

I understand that you took vows, but so did they. If they're not going to stick by their vows and go through with it, why should you have? Why should you have to make it work when the other person isn't putting in their work, their effort? No one wants to be divorced, but sometimes we make mistakes & we shouldn't have to be stuck with that mistake for the rest of our lives.

YOU ARE NOT REQUIRED TO MAKE ANY
RELATIONSHIP WORK THAT'S CAUSING MORE
HARM THAN GOOD OR IS A TOXIC RELATIONSHIP.

There will be tough times in relationships that you should fight to make work, but being mistreated intentionally, being disrespected, made a fool of, any kind of abuse, or being belittled is not a relationship work fighting for or making it work.

.'

<u>REMINDER.</u>

Stop letting people get away with hurting you, making you sad, making you question yourself & your worth.
Open your mouth and speak up when something is bothering you or not okay with you.
You don't like how someone spoke to you, speak up.
You don't like how someone handled this situation involving you, speak up.
You don't like what you're seeing, say something.
People can't change if they don't know there's a problem.
Speak up for yourself no matter who is on that other side.

I should've.
I should've fought harder for me.
I should've stood up & fought for myself.
I should've fought for my worth, my smile, my peace of mind, my happiness.
I should've never let it get this far to the point where I don't feel like me anymore.
I should've never let it get so far that without you, I felt like I was nothing.
They say you should learn to love yourself before you love anyone else.
I used to hate that saying with everything in my body.
It used to make me feel like because I didn't love myself no one else would or no one would find me worthy enough to love.
But that's not true. I think I'm starting to understand it.
I should've loved myself first,
So no one could ever walk in and do what you did to me and to my life.
I should've loved myself first,
So at the first red flag or sign, I could run as fast as I could because I know I'm too good for certain situations.
I should've loved myself first,
So I wouldn't have found myself in a situation begging and pleading for another human being to just love me.
I should've loved myself.
But I didn't. I became so reliant on you for everything that had to do with me.
I don't regret it, as much pain as I am right now,
I don't regret you, us, or anything that we went through.
I should've just done better by me.
And because of you, because of this, because of us, I will.

<u>Because of you.</u>
Because of you, I have never felt pain like I felt with you.
I have never felt so low.
I have never hated myself the way I did when it came to you.
I have never been so broken.
At the same time.
Because of you, I had to learn how to lean on myself.
I learned how to hold & comfort myself.
I learned how to pick myself back up.
I learned how to wipe my own tears away & keep moving forward.
I learned how to be alone and be okay with it.
Because of you, I had to get back on my feet.
I had to learn how to re-love myself.
I had to break the last of myself down and rebuild.
And as much I hate to say it,
Because of you, because of everything that we went through,
I finally got myself back.

Reminder.
You matter!
You are here for a reason.
You matter!
You are here for a reason.
You matter!
You are here for a reason.
You matter to me.
Please believe it.

Why is it enough when time is up?

'Why is it that every time I've finally had enough, or every time I've packed my bags to leave is when you finally get up and be the man that I've wanted all this time? Why is it never enough to want to be better on a good day? Why am I not worthy enough for you to pull it together while I'm there? I don't want to have to keep doing this. I don't want to have to get to threatening to walk out the door for you to get yourself together. If I'm not what you want or need please just leave me instead of constantly having me question myself when I'm with you. I love you, but I need to be enough for you while we're here, together & I don't need to be with you at all.'

Why don't people I love fight for me as hard as I do for
them?

'I fight so hard for people that I love. I go over and beyond
for them. I'd move mountains. I'd fight through hell and back
for them. I'd do whatever it takes for people when I love and
care about them. Whatever, whenever, however, it takes I'm
there, ready for war, ready to hold them, ready to protect
them, ready to wipe their tears, everything and anything I'm
there without a shadow of a doubt. So why when I need these
same people, they're gone? Why at the slightest bit of
inconvenience or hardship these people that I love and would
do anything for are turning their backs on me so quickly?
Why when one small grey cloud starts rolling in they don't
care to even look back and check on me as their running
away? I guess what hurts is that the same people I would
almost die for don't even know when I'm down or not myself.
The same people I would kill for are the ones quick to find
an easy way out when things get a little difficult even if it
means throwing me under the bus. It's crazy, right? The same
people I love clearly don't love me back, at least not the way
that I love them.'

<u>I gave.</u>
I gave too damn much.
I gave my happiness.
I gave my worth.
I gave my peace of mind.
I gave myself.
I gave all of my power.
That's the thing about love,
They tell you to give and give and give until you have
nothing left.
That's when you know you really fought for a relationship,
for love.
What they never tell you are the consequences of giving too
much.
The consequences you face when you give & give & give
and it's still not enough, it still doesn't work out.
What are you left with?
I mean you gave your happiness away, your worth, your
peace of mind, yourself and all of your power.
You gave it all away for love.
All of it, gone.
You leave with nothing.
They never tell you that there should be a limitation on how
much to give or at least what you give.
That when you love someone, of course, you're supposed to
fight and give it your all, but to what extent?
Love will have its hardships, that's a guaranteed fact.
But what kind of love are you really fighting for if it
requires you having to give core parts of you that should
never be bothered or up for debate?

What kind of love are you fighting for if it means giving up your peace of mind, your happiness, your worth, and your mental health?
I mean really think about it.
I'll tell you.
A love that isn't worth a second more of your time.

REMINDER.

One day you're going to wake up
And the pain won't hurt as much,
The tears won't fall as fast,
And you'll be okay.

'Just give you a chance to explain right? Let you explain everything and it'll all make sense right and I would have no reason to be in tears right now? That's it right? So you can make a stupid excuse as to why you did what you did and add a bunch of "I'm sorrys" "I love yous" "It was just a mistake" "You were just feeling lonely" and more in there to make it seem as if you really love me. But see the difference between me and you is that when I say I love you, my actions speak loud and clear. I got out every day in a world full temptations, bad decisions prepared to take place, and so many different ways and different things arise to try to discredit the love that I have for you and I never take it. I never folded. I never take it because I know what I have, I know what we're working towards, I know where we could be and it's never been worth wrecking, at least to me. I've never folded when it came to the love I had for you. The difference between when I say I love you and you say you love me is that I could never hurt you, I could never put you in a position where you look stupid, where you have to suffer on account of my choices. I just wish you loved me that same way in return. So save it. Keep your excuses and your "I love yous" to yourself. Keep your apologies to yourself because I really don't care anymore. You had every opportunity to prove it, and you failed, again.'

I've lost myself.

Isn't it crazy how one minute you've got your whole life figured out, you know exactly who and what you want to be and you're ready to take on the world by storm?

Then slowly but surely you wake up every day and it's getting harder and harder to recognize who you are anymore.

I don't know how I let it get this far.

For some reason, I can't pinpoint the exact moment, but here I am.

Alive but not living.

I'm here but not really here.

I can't even put into words who or what I am right now.

The person I used to be, the person I thought I would be is just gone, just like that.

With no note, no goodbyes, no warning, just gone.

I've completely lost myself.

& I have no idea how I lost her or how to get her back.

She's all I see when I look at you.

'No! This isn't something you can just waltz in with your charm and your smile and fix. You can't just try to make me laugh and think I'll forget or I'll go easier on you. You don't get it. You see as much as I want to forgive you and forget this, I can't! I can't do it no matter how hard I try. You see every time I look at you, every time I look in your eyes I see her. I see her and I hate you even more for it. I can't get the image of her and you out of my head. This is all your fault. As much as I love you and I want to be with you, I don't see you in that light anymore. I don't recognize you anymore. I can't put myself through this where I'm constantly questioning you or even myself. I don't want to feel like I wasn't enough and if I stay, and that's exactly what's going to happen if I do. You made your bed. I just hope you can sleep with everything you've done because you're going to have to live with that forever without me. I hope she was worth losing everything for.'

How do I find myself again?

o   Wanting to find yourself again is the first step. Understanding that you've lost yourself and willing to do whatever it takes to get back to who you once were or a better version of who you once were. Sometimes we get lost in the fact that we lost ourselves we lose all hope of ever being that person again so we give up, we allow the person that we are right now to fill this permanent hole in who we are.

o   Awareness.
So you're getting out of a toxic relationship that took everything out of you? Just by simply realizing you needed change is taking the first step. So you lost your job? Sometimes we're complacent and God refuses for us to settle when we've got bigger things to accomplish. So the environment that you're in has caused you to lose focus and essentially lose yourself? Understanding how harmful and detrimental the environment you're in it for you is taking a very good step in the right direction. Sometimes we pressure ourselves to take these huge steps and when we can't, we shut down. Taking the smallest simplest step is a step.

o   Understanding.
You're going to lose people you've loved, you're going to lose things you've loved, and you're going to lose quite a bit more when you're on this journey. You're going to break down, you're going to be hurt, you're not going to want to let go because you feel like in a way you're losing everything. There's a price to pay for everything, including finding yourself.

46

o   The Reward.

Nothing compares to discovering who you are, what you want and what ignites your soul. Yes, you lose a lot on this journey but you what you gain in the process is worth it all. You gain your peace of mind, you gain happiness, and most importantly you gain yourself. That's worth any and everything in the world you could've ever lost. Be fearless in the pursuit of what sets your soul on fire. You deserve it.

'Why would you stay?'

'You don't get it do you? You'll never understand it. I stay because I love him. I love him and at my lowest points, my darkest moments he was there when no one else was, when everyone turned their backs on me, when everyone was too busy worrying about their own lives, when no one even bothered to check on me, when no one cared, when no else was there, he was. You may not like him, you may not like who he is or some of the things that he's done to me, but he was there. Even you, when you weren't there, he was. So yea, he may have some imperfections, he may not be perfect, he's got some things he needs to work on to become a better man and he's got a lot of growing up to do, but when I needed someone, he was there. And I can't give up on him just because he's not who you want me to be with or he's not the perfect man. I stick around because I love him and he was there.'

'Why would you stay?' Response.

'So you feel like you owe him right? Because at your lowest point he was there so you feel you owe him everything. I mean you have to stay by his side, you have to ride this ride out because he was there when no one else was. But you see what you didn't add to that beautiful speech of yours is that the majority of those bad times that you needed someone there for, he caused them. Those dark and low moments that you went through, it was all because of him. The reason that no one bothered to check on you or you felt no one cared enough about you to do so is because of him. Because of what you let him do to you, you let him pull you away from everyone that loves you and whenever it's up for discussion you shut down, you get mad, and you walk away. So you're right, he was there when no one else was, but make sure you include the fact after pushing all of us away for him, he was the only one left to be there for you.'

REMINDER.

Time isn't a valid excuse as to why you should stay in any relationships or friendships that do more harm than good.
Time isn't a valid excuse as to why you have to make it work with this person.
Time isn't a valid excuse as to why it's okay to be hurt over and over again because of their mistakes.
Time isn't a valid excuse to stay.
Time means nothing if it's costing you your worth, happiness or peace of mind.
Just because you have a history or you've known this person for a long time doesn't make it okay for them to continuously hurt you and get away with it.

I've outgrown you.

'I've outgrown you. Never thought I'd see the day where I could have you back, but I just don't want you back. You left & it hurt me like hell, but as time went by I realized I could do this without you. I didn't need you, I never did. I gave you too much of my power, but now that I'm gaining it all back I don't want to risk losing that with you again. It took me some time, but getting just the smallest taste of being happy with myself, by myself is the one of the most amazing feelings ever. Getting out there trying new things, getting into things that I've always wanted to but was too afraid or was too busy fighting with you to do so. I feel like this whole time I wasted time, precious valuable time that I'll never get back and I can't, I won't sacrifice that for anybody anymore, especially you. Can you believe there's life out there outside of you for me? Ha-ha, I'm done going backwards. I'm moving forward. I'm going to heal myself, love myself, and be the best version of myself. I deserve that & I hope you understand that.'

'Second place.'

I was always second place when it came to you.
For some reason, there was always someone or something
better than me out there for you.
There was always someone prettier, someone more
exciting, or someone who fit your type better than I did.
There was always something more important, something
that held more value, or something that made you happier
than I did.
I used to think that I was going crazy, that I made all of this
up in my head for so long.
And for such a long time I held that with me.
I felt like I wasn't worthy of being someone's first choice.
If I wasn't going to be anyone's first place I might as well
stick around in the second place I've been comfortable with
for so long now.

I Lied.
I lied when I said I was done.
I lied when I said I was over it.
I lied when I said I was moving on.
I lied when I said I was letting go.
I lied.
I tried to force myself to believe a reality that wasn't true.
Hoping that one day, maybe just maybe I'll be able to wake up and believe it.
I'm broken more than I've ever been broken before.
Trying to force myself to be strong and to be "over it" because that's what everyone tells me to do,
But I think it's just made this an even longer painful process.
I lied.
I'm not done.
I'm not over it.
I'm not moving on.
I'm not letting go.
I'm just here.
Dealing with a pain I've never dealt with before.
Suffering in silence because I know no one wants to hear about it anymore.
I lied.
I want to be strong.
I want to be done.
I want to be over it and you.
I want to let go.
I want to get past this and move on.
This is just so much harder than I ever could've imagined.

Pain.
I feel knives.
I feel sharp knives stabbing me in my stomach.
I can't breathe without smelling your scent.
I can't think without seeing your face.
I can't sort through my emotions now, it makes it all too real.
But there's one emotion that's clear,
In a whirlwind of emotions,
One is evidentially clearer than them all
Pain.
Have you ever truly felt your heart breaking into tiny pieces and felt every piece drop into your stomach?
Every tiny piece that drops feels like tiny knives stabbing me, reminding me.
All I feel is pain.
All I think of is pain.
All I am now is pain.

You never loved me.

'You never loved me. You never cared. You never wanted this, at least not the way I did. I would've gone through hell and back for you, and I never felt that feeling being reciprocated. I think that's what hurts the most is that I would've done anything for you and you were just dealing with me, settling for me. I should've walked away a long time ago, but love made me stay. Love made me fight. **I guess love without loving myself first made me easy prey for little boys like you.**'

REMINDER.

Do not confuse the fact that someone keeps running back to you as love or them "realizing what they had."
They didn't come running back because they missed you.
They came back because they missed how you made their ego feel.
They didn't come running back because they love you.
They came back because it's easy getting what they want from you when they need it.
They didn't come running back they missed what you did for them.
They came back because the minimum you allowed isn't enough for anyone else out there, especially one who knows who they are & what they want.
You are worth so much more than someone who chooses to use you or comes running back when it convenient for them.

Do you think about anyone but yourself?

'Did you ever for a second think what you coming back would do to me? Do you ever think about anybody but yourself? Oh so now you're ready to step up, I have to drop everything, stop my life and come running back to you? Did you ever stop to think "damn, I left her, I turned my back on her, and how is this going to affect her?" All you ever do, all you ever did was think about yourself, nothing's changed. For once did you not think "you know what she's been doing fine without me this long, let me not interrupt what she's got going on because damn she does seems & looks happy now." I was doing so well & here you are, ready to open back up old wounds. When you left, I had to pick myself back up, glue the pieces of my life or whatever was left and move forward. So no, I don't give a damn about what you have to say or your weak apologies that have no sincerity in them. You didn't see it. You didn't see the aftermath. You didn't see all it took out of me, all it took for me to get back on my feet, but here you are being as selfish as usual. No one's life matters but your own. No one's plans matter but your own. Well, you know what, you've made your bed all these years, now it's time for you to lie down and suffer the consequences for the choices you made.'

<u>You just don't do it for me anymore.</u>
I had our whole lives planned in my head of what we were
going to do & be.
I loved you despite your flaws, despite the ugly sides of
you no one saw.
I sacrificed so much of me for you. I compromised myself
for you.
I allowed you to treat me however you wanted and told
myself,
"You love him, just ride it out."
And I guess I was content with that, then.
But I've spent so much time in tears and alone in this
relationship
It's given me so much time to think and evaluate.
This isn't what I want anymore.
I'm not okay with this.
You don't do it for me anymore.
It's crazy how much pain it took from you to get me to this
point,
Because I never imagined my life without you.
And the thought of being alone, being without you, it once
terrified me.
But here I am, and now
The thought of being without you not only is okay with me,
but it gives me so much peace of mind now.
You don't do it for me anymore.
Growth is such a beautiful thing after the rough and ugly
sides.
One minute you find yourself willing to tolerate anything
for love,
And the next you find yourself looking in the mirror like,

58

"What the hell have you gotten yourself into and allowed for so long?"
So no, you don't do it for me anymore.
Actually, you haven't done it for me in a while,
I guess the fear of what was out there outside of you kept me inside this little box.
But I've outgrown this small confined box, this life with you, and most importantly you.
So I really do wish you all the best in the world and I hope you do the same for me.
Thank you for everything, good and bad.
Next.

REMINDER.

I know it's hard, but it's time to forgive them.
Not for them, but for you.
Take your life back, take your peace of mind back, and take your power back.
Don't allow someone who hurt you to dictate every decision you make going forward in your life.
Don't allow them to be the 'because this person hurt me, I'm going about it this way instead of the way I would've gone about it before them.'
Take the weight off of your shoulders;
The stress off of your mind.
No one deserves to have that much control over your life.

I deserve so much better than this; then you.

I deserve someone who wants to make me smile instead of cry.

Someone who instead of picking at my insecurities, they reassure me that those insecurities of mine are what they love and admire the most about me.

I deserve someone who knows what they want.

Someone who isn't playing games with my heart and my mind because they're unsure of what they need out of life.

I deserve someone who not only says the love me but proves it every second of every day, every time they get the chance.

I deserve happiness.

I deserve love, good genuine love.

Although I've allowed bad time and time again,

This is it.

I'm standing my ground.

It's time for me to starting fighting for what I deserve.

Now you realize what you had?

'Oh, so now you realizing everything huh? You're realizing what you had, you're realizing that not everyone out in the world is going to do what I did for you. After everything I've sacrificed, everything I compromised including myself, all the patience, time, love, all of that, now you realized how special I was. Did it take you breaking me down to the point of no return? After everything I've done to keep us afloat and everything you've done to try to drown us, me leaving was it? Well, you know what? I've realized something too. I don't want to have to be broken down to pieces for you to realize my value. I don't want to have to walk away from you every time I start to feel taken advantage of for you want to fix it, to realize what you have and what I do for you. I don't want this life of pain anymore to get to the smallest tiniest bit of love from you. I don't want it. I'm glad now that you've realized everything I bought to the table. I'm glad that you've seen the value that I've added to your life. I'm just sad that I have to be drained, broken, or ruined by you for you to realize that.'

We are not on your terms only anymore.

'You don't get to pick and choose when you're in and when you're out when it's convenient for you anymore. I've had it up to here with you having all the power and taking advantage of it every chance that you get. I've realized now that I've given you way too much power, over us, over me, over my happiness, over my life. This is where I draw the line. You've had every opportunity to decide exactly what it is that you want and instead you've selfishly chosen to suck me as dry as possible and leave me with nothing. They say time tells all, and I'm grateful for all the time I wasted here with you because **I will never waste another second of my time fighting for someone's love who's intentionally and unapologetically putting me through a war for their own satisfaction.**'

REMINDER.

Don't let them break you.
Don't let them ruin you.
Don't let them take or keep that power over you.
Don't let them steal that smile of yours.
Don't let them rob you of that joy.
Don't let them keep you fueled up with anger.
You are so special, whether you believe it or not.
I want you to know that despite what you've gone through.
You can choose to still love, to still laugh, to be happy.
You are worth so much more than you ever could've imagined.
Don't let them win.
This is your life.
Take it back.

You aren't worth fighting for anymore.
I've tried to fight this feeling for so long.
We've spent so much time together and because of that, I've tried to make it work.
I've sacrificed, I've compromised, I've drained myself completely empty fighting for you.
The end results are something I can no longer stand by.
I let time and the love I once had for you make me feel like I had to stay.
You are going to be an amazing person and partner,
For someone else.
You & I both know it shouldn't be like this.
The good times shouldn't occur once in a while.
I think **we loved each other so much that we made the toxicity that we both were to & for each other the new normal**.

We're holding each other back.
At one point I saw forever with you, with us.
We had the same visions, taking the same routes, we wanted the same end results.
But lately we've been distant, that feeling of disconnect gets louder every day.
We've steered away from each other, along with our lives and dreams and paths.
You've got such big dreams and plans for your life,
And I would never want to get in the way of that especially seeing how happy it makes you.
But at the same time so have my dreams.
Our dreams have gotten bigger & they just don't coincide anymore.
I never thought you could feel yourself growing apart from someone you love.
Especially when we had such big plans with each other.
You can feel the separation no matter how hard I tried to ignore it.
We've outgrown each other's lives.

Dear old me.

I just, I want to apologize to you. I'm so sorry. I'm so sorry about what I allowed. I'm so sorry for thinking so less of you. I apologize from the bottom of my heart for questioning you & your worth. You deserved so much better & it breaks my heart knowing that I put you through what you went through. I just wanted to write you to let you know all those years of suffering, of feeling worthless, of being sad, or feeling numb did some good in the long run. I finally see what you wanted to see so badly in you. That heart of yours is so pure & filled with gold, I see that now. The way you love and the way you care for others, I know how much of a curse it felt like then for you, but turns out when you're a little cautious, pay attention, follow your heart & bring your brain along with you, it's a pretty amazing experience. There are so many amazing things about you that you didn't even recognize because you were so focused on those negatives. You hated them then, and I've grown to love them now. So I didn't write you this letter so you can go back down memory lane and remember those painful moments, I'm writing you in hopes that I can finally give you some peace in that life of chaos & misery you once were.

Sincerely,
The New Me.

YOU ARE NOT DAMAGED GOODS.
You've gone through some tragic incidents.
None of which you deserved.
You've suffered through situations no one should ever have
to witness or endure,
But you are not damaged goods.
You are a fighter, better yet, you're a survivor, and you're a
warrior.
You deserve happiness, you deserve love, and you deserve
peace.
No one may ever understand what you went through,
But whatever it is, it doesn't erase or lower your value or
your worth.
You are just as valuable, you are just as worthy, and you
are just as deserving.
YOU ARE NOT DAMAGED GOODS.

<u>REMINDER.</u>

You can't change what could've been, what would've been
or what should've been.
All you have is right now.
So what are you going to do about it so you don't have to
sit back another couple years from now and think about
what could've, would've or should've been?
The choice is up to you.

<u>I know</u>
I know I gave you everything I had in me.
From my blood to my sweat, to my tears, to my heart, to my soul,
To the very last drop of myself, I gave it all to you.
I put so much of my trust into you,
That **I was willing to lose myself to keep you, to keep us.**
I know I gave you everything I had in me.
Because I can't recognize myself anymore.
I guess I gave so much of me away to you,
I don't know who I am anymore without you.
I know I gave you everything I had in me.
This is what they say love consists of right?
Fighting to the point of no return, giving everything you have in you.
To make it work.
I know I gave you everything I had in me.
You left and now there's no me.
I know.

All I ever wanted was for you to fight for me.
For you to scream from the rooftops that you love me &
would do anything it took for me to be with me, to hold me
in your arms and say I was your everything.
For you to put me first and do everything in your power to
protect me.
For you to tell me how amazing I was, how lucky you were
& for you to love me.
You never did.
As I sit back today I've realized something.
And you know what?
Maybe I should've fought for myself as hard as I wanted
you to fight for me.
You know? Maybe I should've screamed from the rooftops
that I loved me so you knew that if you weren't ready to
walk in and give me that same energy you wouldn't last.
Maybe I should've put myself first and do everything in my
power to protect me even from the people I loved the most.
Maybe I should've told myself how amazing I was and
believed it.
Or you know what? Maybe I was asking for too much from
you.
Maybe this was all too much for you, or maybe I was just
asking the wrong person.
Maybe I should've asked more from myself before I asked
anyone else.
Maybe I should've loved me first.

REMINDER.
You are beautiful.
You are amazing in every kind of way possible.
You are worth everything good in this world.
You just have to believe it.

Why waste my time if you weren't interested?

'Why didn't you want this? Me? Us? What made her so special? What made her worth losing everything over? What did I do to you? I don't deserve this. I don't deserve this especially from you. Everything I sacrificed for you. Everything I gave up for you. I wiped your tears away on your worst days and cheered loudest for you on your best days. What the fuck did I do so wrong to you for you to put me through this? What am I supposed to do now? Why wasn't I enough for you? Why did you have to ruin everything?'

There's nothing wrong with taking some alone time to yourself to figure you out.
No one wants to be alone forever,
But at some point, everyone has to learn how to be content and happy with themselves first.
When you don't learn how to be happy with yourself, you start to lean onto others for that happiness, and you start allowing whatever to keep that happiness.
When you learn to be okay with being alone, you learn that you being alone is far better than dealing with relationships & friendships that are toxic to you.
Learn to be alone so you don't ever need anyone, especially anyone who's detrimental to you, your happiness, your mental health or your peace of mine.
If you don't like being with you, how can you expect anyone else to?

Loving you isn't enough anymore.

'It's not enough anymore. Loving you and you loving me. It's just not enough anymore. I was told that when you love someone and they love you back, that's all that matters and everything else will fall into place or you can worry about everything later. In some cases they're right, they're 100% right. But I'm here with you right now knowing that I love you, knowing that you love me, and yet we're miserable. It's not enough, sometimes it's just not enough. I don't want either of us to love each other so much that we're willing to just slide certain things under the rug and hope it'll just go away someday. I don't want either us to wake up one day, look at each other and end up resenting one another. We both deserve to love & to be enough, and maybe just maybe we're not enough for each other.'

REMINDER.

It's okay to cry.
It's okay to be sad.
It's okay to feel like today is a bad day.
It's okay to admit that life is a little fucked up right now.
It's okay to just not be okay.
Don't let the world make you feel like having low moments
makes you weak.
It makes you human.

The low.

'I don't want to care anymore. I don't want to love. I don't want to open my heart up. I'm done getting back out here just to get tripped and fall flat on my face. I'm tired. I've never felt more exhausted in my life. Physically, mentally, emotionally I'm done. I'm not even a person anymore, I feel like a waste of life. I feel like a ghost. No one sees me, no one understand me, and no one gets it. I'm just here, left to pick up all the pieces, dealing with all the aftermath. I've never felt so numb in my life. I mean if this can be an outcome of loving, what's the point? What's the rush? Why do people want it so badly? My heart hurts so badly.'

I used you as an escape goat.

'I thought that if I could work overtime to just make you happy, that eventually we'd be happy & then I'd be happy. I thought that with time everything would eventually be okay if I kept fighting for us. I think I was wrong though. I think maybe I put too much on your plate that wasn't for you to have to deal with. Maybe I put too much of my weight & pressure on your shoulders. It's so much of myself I needed working on and I think I confused it with or tried to diffuse it by working so much on us. I thought if I could just turn my attention onto something else, I wouldn't have to deal with these problems, but here I am. I think I just needed you as a scapegoat. Someone I can run to and try to fix to run away from my problems and I think I'm just now realizing that I still have to face these problems whether I want to or not.'

REMINDER.

You can't make them care about you.
You can't make them love you.
No matter how much you care or love them back if they
don't, they don't.
Don't spend your time trying to force people to be a part of
your life.
You deserve better than them, and you deserve a lot better
from yourself.
Do better by you.

You really think I need you?

'You selfish boy. You think I need you? You think I can't make it or I can't be happy without you? Maybe I play a pretty big role in the reason why you think that. I've allowed certain things and basically started to rely on you for everything; my happiness, my life, etc. & for that, I am slightly to blame, but I'm stronger now. You think you defeated me, you think you've won. You've beaten me down, made me question myself, lose myself, hate myself, and for a while, I was broken. I never could've imagined myself getting back on my feet and I know that was your biggest fear; me not needing you. But here I am, stronger than I've ever been. I don't need you, I don't want you, and I want nothing to do with you. Now I get to walk away with my head held high because I took my life back, I won.'

Sometimes we have to let the people that we love go.
Not because we don't care, not because we don't love them,
but sometimes the people we love the most do the most
harm to us.
We accept it and tolerate it because we love them and don't
want to lose them.
It's hard, realizing that some of the people that we love just
aren't meant to be in our lives forever.
But eventually, you're going to have to put your heart first
and remove people who do more bad than good, people
who hurt us, people who use us, etc.
Sometimes we have to love the people we love from a
distance.

WHAT'S THE POINT OF LOVING?

'You know what they never tell you about love is what it does to you when it doesn't work out. They never explain to you the pain and loss you feel when you love someone and they don't love you back or they break your heart. They describe it as the beautiful thing that makes you smile and laugh but never explain the times that you cry, scream and in pain. What's the point of falling in love if this is how it ends every single time? I always end up either in pain, questioning myself, hating myself, or just feeling flat out numb. I don't want to do this again. I'm so tired of putting myself and my heart through this for what? For nothing. He's gone and I hate life, I hate myself, I hate the thought love. I don't want this anymore. If this is how love ends, I don't want this.'

WHAT'S THE POINT OF LOVING? (RESPONSE)

'So you dated a couple of times and got your heart broken. So it didn't end the way you expected to. So love is a lot tougher than you imagined. It's life. The point is one day, it's all going to make sense. Why it never worked out with anyone else. No one ever explained this side of love to you, because it's different for everybody. Not everyone gets that happy ending their first couple of tries, and some people get that happily ever after on their first try. No one is ever going to be able to explain how love works, because no one really knows. But one thing we can all come to a conclusion of is the alternative of love, not loving at all is worse than loving and getting hurt. So it's tough, and no one has the exact answers that you'd want to hear on what's the point of loving, but we've got our experiences, we've loved, and we've determined that whatever the answer to that question is, it's worth getting out there, loving and fighting for.'

REMINDER.

It's okay to miss someone, even if they were bad.
Whether people understand it or not, you were there
through the good & the bad.
It's okay to miss the good parts, moments, memories of
someone while letting them and the bad go.

You used me.
You used me to boost your ego up.
You used me to drag down so you could feel lifted.
You used me as your punching bag to take all the hits while you stood in the victory.
So I'm going to use you.
Not in the selfish way you chose to use me though.
See I'm going to use you as an example.
I'm going to use you as to how low it can get when I don't put myself first.
I'm going to use you as a reminder, to never let it get as bad as you were.
I'm going to use you so I can finally do some good in my life, in myself.

You came back.
You finally came back.
I should be ecstatic right now,
This is the moment I've been waiting for since the second you left.
For you to come running back into my arms,
For you to have realized what you lost, to hold me tight and never let me go.
It's here, you came back for me.
Past parts of me want to jump in rejoice because she always dreamed of the day you came running back.
A part of now me wants you to understand, **I'm not the same woman you left behind** that day you turned your back and walked away.
Trust me I'm still broken.
Parts of me I can feel from within that I'll never be able to recover from.
Parts of me are going to take moving mountains just for me to heal from and let go of.
Parts of me never wants to allow another in enough to hurt me, the way you did.
You broke me.
In the midst of being alone with all these sad little broken pieces of me scattered everywhere.
I've found some time to start rebuilding some of those pieces,
Stronger pieces of me to build a stronger foundation.
You came back to a new version of me.
A stronger, still a lot is broken, but a wiser version of me.
So although it feels good to know that you came back.
It feels even better to say,
You came back too late.

REMINDER.

There's nothing wrong with having a huge heart.
There's nothing wrong with loving with everything in your heart & soul.
But with such a great gift as such, comes great responsibility.
You have to be very particular with who you choose to love and give your time to.
We can't choose who we love, but we can decide who's worthy enough for you to give your heart, time & dedication to.

Sometimes karma won't get them back.
Sometimes they won't ever feel bad for hurting you.
Sometimes they will never care about you or what you've done for them.
It's the sad honest truth.
Sometimes people do hurtful things & never feel sorry about it.
But life doesn't stop & neither should you.
Stop waiting for them to get their karma.
Stop waiting for them to get "what they deserve."
Start working on you.
Start working on not allowing what you don't deserve.
Start working on learning from your mistakes so you don't go down that route again.
Work on you.

<u>I wish I could forget you.</u>
I wish I could forget your face,
For all the times I looked at your face & fell in love with
your smile and eyes all over again.
I wish I could forget your voice,
For all the times it gave me comfort on my best days & my
worst days.
I wish I could I forget your scent because for some odd
reason when I start to miss you your scent just runs through
me,
I wish I could forget ever meeting you,
Because that moment replays in my head every time I think
I'm over you and I take steps backward.
I wish I could forget all the bad between you and me,
Because it definitely outweighed all the good we ever
shared together.
And I hate to say this,
Because I know we should never regret people & memories
because without them we wouldn't be who we are right
now,
But I wish I could forget all the good too,
Because the good times make me hate you even more for
all the bad times you put me through.
Most importantly I wish I could forget you,
So I can forget why I've built these walls surrounding me
that whoever chooses to enter my life will have to climb to
get even the slightest bit from me.
I just really wish you never walked into my life to begin
with.
I wish I could forget you so I can finally have the peace &
happiness that I once did far before you ever came into the
picture.

REMINDER.
Be loyal to yourself.
Fight for yourself.
Love yourself.
Move mountains for your worth, your dreams, yourself.
Sometimes everything we find ourselves begging for from another human being is what we need to learn to beg from out of ourselves.
If we can't fight for ourselves and what we deserve.
How can we ever expect another to do it?
In fact, how can we ever expect another to know what we deserve if we don't even know what we deserve?

I forgive you.
I forgive you for hurting me.
For making me feel so worthless.
For making me constantly question myself.
I forgive you.
For not knowing how to love me.
For not trying to learn how to love me.
For not caring to try to love me better.
I forgive you.
For not seeing me worthy in your eyes to be the best
version of yourself.
For not being affected in the slightest way when it came to
me being in pain.
I forgive you.
For being young.
For not being ready.
For not knowing any better.
I forgive you,
Because I'm so tired of blaming you for everything wrong
with me to this day.
Because I'm tired of being angry.
Because I'm exhausted with being so damn bitter all the
damn time.
I forgive you.
Because I want my life back.
I want to be happy again.
I want to smile, laugh, joke, and not have to be the worst
unhappiest version of myself because of the decisions that
you made & the decisions that I chose to stick around for.
I'm done fighting you when you've been long gone.
I'm forgiving me,
And I forgive you.

<u>I wanted you.</u>

I wanted you.

I wanted you to be there for me.

I wanted you to wipe my tears away.

I wanted you to hold me close in your arms and never let me go.

I wanted you to tell me that everything was going to be okay even if you knew deep down in your heart that it wasn't going to be even close to okay.

I wanted you to love me, not just say it to make yourself or make me feel good, but love me because that's what your heart wanted, to love me.

I wanted you to mean it, mean it with every bone in your body.

Because when you love someone, you don't just leave.

You don't see dark clouds rolling in and take off without me.

You don't see someone you love down and walk away.

I wanted you to fight for me.

Fight with everything you had in you because you knew when it came down to it, I would've done the same thing for you.

But you left.

The rain started coming down and you ran as fast as you could with your tail tucked between your legs and you never looked back, not even for me.

I wanted so much out of you, yet I felt like I was begging for you to just be there for me.

<u>REMINDER.</u>
Learn to stop letting people take advantage of your heart.
People know exactly what they're doing.
They know right from wrong.
They know if the roles we reversed, they'd be mad at you
for doing what they're doing to you right now.
Learn to make your heart a priority.
If they can't do right by your heart, they don't deserve a
spot in your life.
Especially when there are people out there that will cherish
the ground you walk on.
You want people to take your love & heart serious?
Maybe you need to be the first to do so.

Growth can be ugly.

No one ever discusses the ugly sides of growth and loving yourself.

Going back in your mind, reliving traumatic childhood memories, forgiving people who you feel don't deserve it because of what they've done to you, breaking old toxic traits and patterns you've learned through generations of family. It's not easy. Letting go of your daddy issues that's caused you to be in relationships fighting for a man to stay to fill that void of not having a father. Forgiving those parents who abandoned you for drugs, another man or woman, or for another family that has you in relationships trying to save people who clearly doesn't care about you when you're really trying to save your parents or have you in relationships trying to keep people who don't want to be kept trying to fill that void.

It's not easy.

Looking in the mirror and pointing out your flaws.

The flaws that you've made up in your head based off of insecurities, but the flaws you've established off of the traumas and situations you had to endure that were never your fault or your choice.

The flaws that people have pointed out that makes you standout, the flaws that are your insecurities.

No one speaks on this.

They make you believe growth and the journey to finding & loving yourself is this beautiful journey.

And it's not, at least not at first.

There's so many instances that we suffer in silence or that we teach our minds to block out just so we can make it through the day & through life.

We never deal with them and as life goes on, those instances continuously pop up in & out of your lives never really let us breathe or be free.

It's like chains wrapped around our necks holding us back, allowing us to be alive but never really living.

So this journey is one hell of a journey. It will never be an easy process, dealing with our traumas; but the end result is worth every second of it.

You can be happy again.

You can be free.

But it's a battle you'll have to face despite how ugly that past is.

The past.

The past is such an ugly place to look back on. You see young you making dumb mistakes, ignoring red flags, getting in bad situations, hurting people that you love, you get hurt by people that you care about and all the bad that comes with your past, it's easy for you to let those things ram into your present and even your future. But the beautiful thing about the past is that you can always revisit it in your mind when you need a little reminder on what not to do. People see the past as this horrible place where you were the worst version of yourself. I see the past as a guide, a teaching lesson. Whenever I want I can go back and see the consequences I had to face for my decisions and I can work a thousand times harder now to make sure I never have to face those same consequences again. I never had to make those mistakes anymore. I can do better with my life. I can take a step in a better direction because of my past. You can choose to look at is this horrible place that ruined your life & continues to ruin your life or you can choose to say no. You can choose to move on and let the past be the past and your present be your present and your future be your future. It's up to you.

REMINDER.

Moving on is tough especially when years of your life have
been invested.

Don't push yourself too hard.

It's a process that's going to take time.

Healing from heartbreak is never easy.

Be patient with yourself and more importantly your heart.

<u>I'm sorry.</u>
I'm sorry for trying to change you.
I never realized that putting these expectations on you would make you feel as if you being you wasn't good enough.
I never grasped the pressure I was putting on your shoulders to be someone that you didn't sign up to be.
It wasn't fair to you at all.
& that was never my intention.
But I want you to know that I never looked at it as trying to force you to be someone or something else because I somehow wasn't satisfied with who you are right now.
I looked at is as trying to make sure the person that I love, admire & want the best for so much, to never look back on their life and be unhappy with the choices & the person that they once were.
So with all the best intentions in the world and in my heart, I made a dumb mistake.
Though I won't apologize for seeing something so special in you that I was willing to do whatever it takes for you to not only see it, but for you to be it.
I will absolutely apologize for ever making you feel like you being you wasn't good enough for me, because it is.

I knew I'd instantly cave in.

I'd walk in, look into your eyes and fall right into your arms again.

You may never understand how hard it was for me to leave. And I know you,

I know you're questioning why I walked away and never even looked back.

But I knew if I had stayed one second longer,

If I looked into your eyes one more time,

My mind would go back in time and give me every reason to stay.

I would somewhere somehow fight every reason I had to leave with a reason to stay and I'd end up running back into your arms and I'd stay there forever.

I know me.

I know how you make me.

I know how I get when it comes to you.

If I didn't leave then, if I didn't walk away right then and there & didn't look back I never would've left.

And the same ole cycle would continue again and again and we'd never get out of it.

You're responsible for you own healing, no one else.

I think sometimes we hold people to too much responsibility in our lives. We choose someone to love and we throw them all our baggage and expect them to not only carry it for us, but to take it away. We want them to love all of the bad out of us, we want them to boost our egos, give us that confidence we've been missing. We want them to cure us of all the pain that we've ever endured. We place all of that responsibility and more on them, and when they can't carry all of that weight and they finally break down & fall; we blame ourselves. We punish ourselves. We beat the hell out of ourselves over the fact that this person that we loved couldn't carry or handle our baggage. Then we carry our baggage and the baggage of this person that we love not being able to carry it for us and drag it into another relationship that comes with its own baggage's and the cycle continues. I think we all need to learn that our healing is our responsibility. **We need to stop holding other people who aren't responsible, accountable for our traumas and our unwillingness to heal from those traumas**. The people that we love can only go so long without any effort on our end.

The high.

I get it. I understand everything now. I see why, I see how
everything was meant to play out. I can't believe how bad it
was, how bad I let it get, but I don't know why I just feel
like I needed it though. I needed it to get so bad that I was
nearly broken to realize that I didn't deserve it, any of it.
That feeling of feeling not good enough of feeling empty, I
just I thought then that that was what life was supposed to
feel like & it feels so good to finally know that I deserve
better. I've finally found peace and I don't have to worry
about dumb things anymore, dumb things that you made
me have to use all of my energy on. I just, **I never thought
you could feel so free**. All I've ever known, all I've ever
witnessed is bad and it feel so damn good to finally get
some good, to finally feel good. Maybe they're right,
maybe the low times don't last forever. Maybe there are
some highs after all.

REMINDER.

Fire people.

Nothing can ever run smoothly if you have people who are interrupting the rotation, the environment.

Let them go.

Sometimes we have to take personal feelings out of it, and do what's best for you, your peace of mind and mental health despite how people feel.

Let's be honest, if they loved you, and I mean really loved you, would you be here questioning their presence in your life right now?

I wanted to be "The One" for you so badly.

'I would've done anything to have been the one for you. I know I could've loved you so much. I know I could've valued all that you are, the big or small, the good or bad. I would understand that all of that combined made you into the person that I loved. I could've moved mountains for our love. I could've gone the extra mile. I would've done anything for you to let the world know that I was your one and only. That it was me, it was always me and no one stood a chance or could've gotten in the way. I would've given anything to have been the one in your darkest moments that you'd think of and want to be with you to help cope with it all. I guess the part I wasn't too aware of was thinking that just because I felt that way about you didn't mean that the feelings were going to be mutual. But that's what makes me at peace with this, with me and you. Because I know that if I could feel this strongly about someone, I know for a fact that there's someone out there who can feel just as strongly, if not stronger than I did when it came to you. This love thing can be hell at times. Loving the wrong person, loving someone who refuses to love us back, loving when there's nothing to love. **But I imagine when you find the right one, love can be the most beautiful experience life has to offer** and that right there is worth me letting go and moving on.'

If people are going to make the conscious decision to hurt you.
Meaning they're aware of the consequences that they'll face with this decision.
They're aware of the pain & hurt that this decision will cause you.
They know what's at stake, they know what they could potentially lose
& they choose to make that decision anyways knowing all of that.
You need to make a wise decision being fully aware of those same facts.
They gambled.
They knew they could possibly lose you with this choice, mistake, decision, etc.
& they choose to take that chance anyways.

I'm happier now without you.

'I'm happy now. Like I'm happier than I've ever been in my life now & I can't revert back. I can't turn my life backwards now just because you finally decided that you're ready or that you made a mistake. I gave you chance after chance and **every chance I gave you, you made me feel stupid for caring and choosing to love you.** So no, I'm not trying to show out, prove to you that I've moved on or pretend that I'm happy to show you what you missed out on. If anything that feeling that you're feeling so strongly is a direct line of guilt building up inside of you for how terrible you were & that has nothing to do with me. So blame me all you want, say that I'm living to make you jealous or regretful, say that I'm being spiteful by moving on. Say whatever you want. I don't want revenge, I'm not trying to get back at you. Believe it or not, my life doesn't revolve around you anymore. So if I seem happy, if I seem peaceful, less angry and in less pain now that we're done, I want you to know that you're absolutely correct. Life has had so much more to offer me since I let go of toxic and dead weight in my life.'

To You,

The toughest battle you'll face in life is within yourself, with yourself. How you deal with life, what you tolerate from people all stems from how you feel about you. I've suffered through this journey myself. I know how tough the battle is and how difficult it can get. I also know the feeling of victory. How you can struggle for so long, feeling so low, questioning yourself & work your butt off to get to a position where not only can you tolerate what you see when you look in the mirror, but you love it. The victory feeling of healing from all your traumas and taking your life back into your hands. I am proof. I am proof that it's possible, it can happen and it will happen with all the right steps. I believe in you. I want you to have some faith and believe in you.

Sincerely,
Someone who's been there,

Martine Ashley

Printed in Great Britain
by Amazon

36175777R00069